The Second Leunig

... A DUSTY LITTLE SWAG

All my father left me
Was a dusty little swag
And a pair of tiny booties
In a crumpled paper bag
And he left me in confusion
And he left me in despair
And he left the swag and booties
For the walk to god knows where.

Leunig

The Second Leunig
... A DUSTY LITTLE SWAG

CARTOONS.... A FEW VERSES ... AND SELECTED
MOMENTS FROM THE VOYAGE OF VASCO PYJAMA.

By Michael Leunig

ANGUS
& ROBERTSON
PUBLISHERS

ANGUS & ROBERTSON PUBLISHERS

Unit 4, Eden Park, 31 Waterloo Road,
North Ryde, NSW, Australia 2113, and
16 Golden Square, London W1R 4BN,
United Kingdom

First published in Australia
by Angus & Robertson Publishers in 1979
First published in the United Kingdom
by Angus & Robertson (UK) Ltd in 1981
Reprinted 1979, 1980 (twice), 1983, 1984, 1986

Copyright © Incorporated Newsagencies Company Pty Ltd
and Michael Leunig 1979

National Library of Australia
Cataloguing-in-publication data.

Leunig, Michael,
    The second Leunig.
    ISBN 0 207 14328 5.
    1. Caricatures and cartoons — Australia.
    2. Australian wit and humor, Pictorial I. Title.
741. 59'94

Printed in Shenzhen, China

DRAMATIC SCENE - DIVER TRAPPED BY GIANT CLAM
ON LEDGE OF CITY OFFICE BLOCK

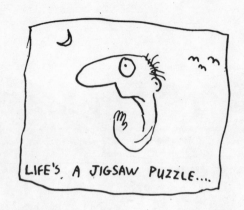

LIFE'S A JIGSAW PUZZLE....

YOU DO IT IN REVERSE.

YOU TAKE A PRETTY PICTURE

AND MAKE IT ALL DIVERSE.

BLAH

Leunig

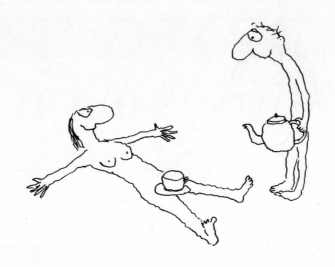

WHY Dogs sniff each others tails.... an old but true story

Once upon a time, when dogs ruled the earth, a gala dog ball was organised and all the dogs in the world were invited...

When the dogs arrived at the ball they checked their tails in at the cloak room as was the custom in those happy, far off days....

It was a wonderful, glittering occasion and all the dogs, regardless of breed or background, danced the night away and were thoroughly enjoying themselves until suddenly......

....the fire alarm sounded. The ballroom was alight and an uproarious panic broke out...

The vast yelping pack stampeded to the cloak room and in the confusion the tails were mixed up

To this day you will see them sniffing each others tails as they go about their forlorn search for their proper tails. This is the eternal aftermath of the night that THE DOG BALL CAUGHT FIRE...!

Leunig

THE DANGERS OF BOAT BUILDING

This is the man whose love of boat building gave way to a passion for bantams which led to an interest in astronomy. Now he is a philosopher.

It seems hard to believe but at last I am dead. I am wrapped in slabs of eucalyptus bark and placed in the branches of some saplings in the manner of an aboriginal grave

It is a mallee landscape. Spring has arrived. I am deeply shattered by the injustice of my own death and very depressed about being confined here for eternity in this itchy, uncomfortable bundle. I am hot and my body is starting to putrify I suspect.

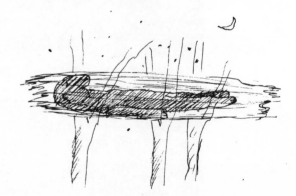

A dusty track winds past the saplings and a straggling group of people move along it. They are young and fresh faced..... they look relaxed and clean. I hear them laughing and talking. Some of them enquire why I am not going to the party.

Somebody holds a mirror up to me and I see that my face is deeply cracked, like the muddy bottom of a dried -up dam. It's quite a shock and my depression worsens. Even if I were alive, I couldn't go to a party looking like this.

→

Suddenly I'm standing at the rear of St. Patricks cathederal in Melbourne. The actor Michael Pate is holding open the door of a crypt and pointing down a grey. cement-brick stairway. He is wearing a black cassock and a clerical collar and is smiling at me.

I peer down the stairway and feel a rush of icy, refrigerated air.... it hurts the cracks in my face. Everything is grey, rough-cast, cement brickwork...... it is modern and featureless.

There are square holes in the walls of the crypt. These are for corpses. Michael Pate is offering me an alternative grave. I am horrified.....dumbfounded by this ugly place and by Pate's benign insensativity. I want to be back in the Mallee.

Then I am back.... wrapped in my bark coffin. in the sapplings. I have made my choice and here I will stay forever and ever. It seems dreadfully unfair. I am so miserable. Outside it is a beautiful day and somewhere there is a party going on.

Leuniy

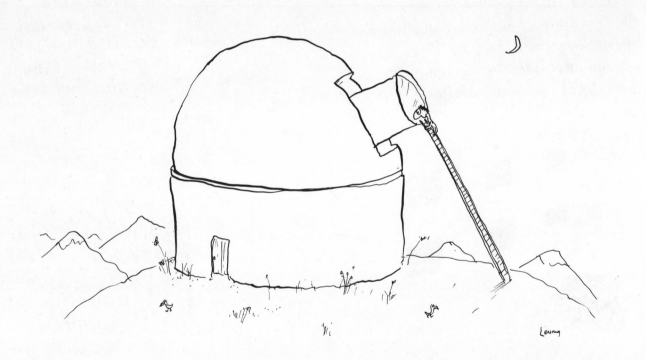

Leunig

DONALD DUCK'S HEAD EXPLODES UNDER THE IMPACT OF AN
ASASSIN'S BULLET DURING A MOTORCADE THROUGH DALLAS,
TEXAS...... LATER, DAISY DUCK MARRIES THE LEADER OF
THE BEAGLE BOYS.

HUGH HEFNER'S PLAYBOY JET NAPALMS THE SURFACE OF THE MOON

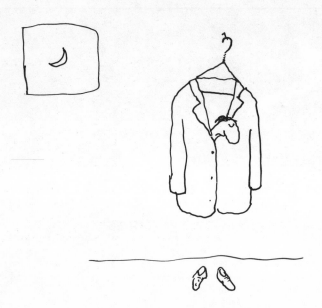

MY SHOE

Since I hurt my pendulum
My life is all erratic.
My parrot who was cordial
Is now transmitting static.
The carpet died, a palm collapsed,
The cat keeps doing poo.
The only thing that keeps me sane
Is talking to my shoe.

Leunig

CHEZ
BIBI
Coiffure

I WANT A
FARRAH FAWCETT-MAJORS
HAIRSTYLE PLEASE...

but sir...
you're bald...

I AM THE MANAGING DIRECTOR
OF THE DEATH RAY CHEMICAL
CORPORATION AND I WANT TO
LOOK LIKE FARRAH
FAWCETT-MAJORS....!

PERHAPS... ERR... PERHAPS WE CAN
STRETCH THE FLESH ON THE SCALP AND
PUT IT IN ROLLERS.... AND... ERR....
COMBINE THE EYEBROWS AND EAR
AND NOSTRIL HAIRS WITH THE WHOLE
KABOODLE.... AND TEASE IT ALL UP
AND...
ERR...

THREE HOURS LATER...

SIZZLING...!

THAT NIGHT HE DINES ALONE AT
THE V.I.P. RESTAURANT WHERE A
WAITER SPILLS A BOWL OF TRIPE
ON HIS NEW HAIRSTYLE

I'M DREADFULLY
SORRY SIR... LET ME
CLEAN IT OFF...

NO...! don't
touch it... you'll
only mess it up
more... I want
it left as it is...

AFTER DINING, HE GOES HOME...

I'm home
dear... notice
anything different?

Yes... you have long flaps
of flesh curled up from your
scalp and it's all mixed up
with tripe and nostril
hairs and white sauce
with parsley and
eyebrows
and you
look just
like...

FARRAH
FAWCETT-
MAJORS...

LET'S GO
TO BED

Leunig

He awoke to find that
his underpants were missing...

He went searching
and met the milkman
who told him that
he had seen a pair
of underpants...

...moving like a
ghost along the foggy
street in the direction
of the paddock...

He ran to the paddock and
there in a ditch he found
the tattered remains of his
underpants...

On his way home he met an
old man who said that last
night he had shot a pair of
marauding underpants which had
been devouring his chickens for
the past two weeks...

At least that explained
the feathers inside his underpants
in recent mornings but it didn't
explain why his life was
degenerating into an uncontrollable
farce.

leunig

KISSES
25¢

SMILES
$2

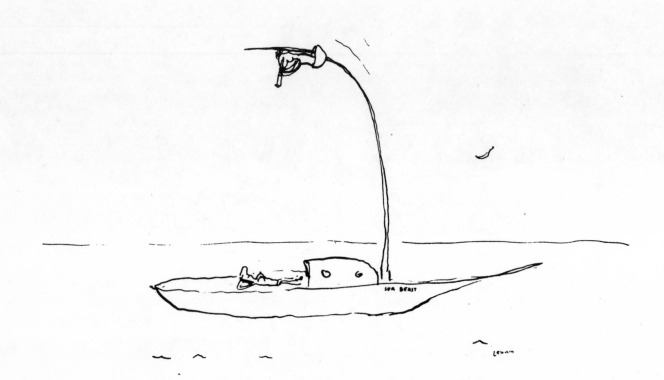

SEA BEAST

The Miracle of Parenthood....

Leunig

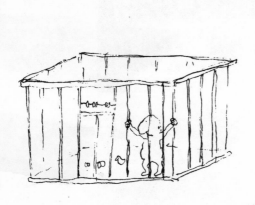

Leunig

Selected Moments
from
The Voyage
of
Vasco Pyjama

Accompanied by his direction-finding duck, Vasco Pyjama bids his parents farewell and rows his amphibious club armchair out of the Curly Flat railway station. So begins the journey which will carry him to the edge of his world.

Vasco Pyjama meets the Fallen Angel who tells him that the only reason angels can fly is because they take themselves so lightly.

Vasco Pyjama's brave and intelligent uncle sets out in search of his·missing nephew.

The scapegoat teaches Vasco Pyjama the art of "copping it sweet" . . . the opposite of self defence.

It seems that Vasco Pyjama has survived the dreaded Strait of a Thousand Lighthouses and has found his way to the Toucan Club. The Toucan Club has long been a peaceful haven for lone voyagers, a place of jubilation and innocently eccentric delights. Lately however, a world-weary despondency has settled on this once happy spot and it now appears that, despite a brave face, the Toucan Club has lost its soul and is dying.

This realisation would capsize Pyjama were it not for the fact that direction-finding ducks always point towards new joys and so Vasco must follow his small, feathered companion in that strange, surprising direction.

. . . and there, standing precariously on a rocky crag was a massive organ inhabited by a colony of large black owls. Its awesome, rapacious pipes being fed with steam which came in long, rolling sighs from a hidden volcanic labyrinth, giving breath for the music played unwittingly by the roosting owls and providing heat for the exotic ferns which festooned this freakish instrument. Vasco Pyjama was gripped with an urge to go to the keyboard and play Fur Elise.

In the quality control section of the mosquito coil factory Vasco Pyjama stumbles on a piece of wisdom with profound practical and philosophical implications. The quality control section is where the coils are checked for cracks as they move along a conveyor belt. Vasco observes that some workers prefer to fix their eyes on the centre of a coil and work their gaze outwards while others seem to start on the outside and let their eyes follow the coil to the centre. Both methods take a terrible toll on the workers. Severe cases of corkscrew neck, cranium spin and twirly vision are common and many manhours are lost while the victims convalesce and unwind.

However Vasco meets a worker who has not missed a day in twenty years and he asks him his secret. "I alternate," says the old man, "inwards then outwards . . . concentric and eccentric . . . no worries."

This perfect and simple wisdom sets Vasco's head spinning with joy. When Vasco's head spins with joy we can be sure that his despair is unwinding.

In a tiny North African town, lone voyager Vasco Pyjama meets the famous writer and philosopher Albert Camus. The night is warm and starry as they sit together on a rooftop overlooking the sea. Albert has been dead for many years but Vasco doesn't seem to mind too much. They sip wine and glimpse the ghostly dhows on the moonlit water below. Conversation flutters away to the desert behind them, shredded by the dry, night wind. You might say it is one of the great, fluttering, wind-shredded conversations. The two dreamers talk of journeys. "A man's work is nothing but the long journey to recover the two or three great and simple images which first gained access to his heart," says Albert smiling into his glass.

(Author's technical note: While Albert's theory may be true in the case of most humans it does not apply to Vasco Pyjama. His life's journey is not a search . . . it is a circumnavigation, which is an entirely different matter. Instead of searching, Vasco drifts in a state of vague wonder with the feeling that perhaps he will finally arrive at those two or three great and simple images where it all began. It is generally believed that those who proceed with vague wonderment will sail off the edge of their world.)

Vasco Pyjama meets Tip Fly . . . an old man who lives in a rubbish tip where all his needs are catered for by the things that people throw away.

Standing amongst his beloved junk Tip Fly proclaims to Vasco his 'theory of disintegration' . . . "Here is the great remorseless inevitability," says Tip Fly . . . "things just seem to fall apart and things are inclined to break." Vasco's direction-finding duck looks up nervously. "Disintegration is a curious business," continues Tip Fly, "some things such as china dinner sets are inclined only to break . . . they rarely fall apart, whereas something like a memory or a knitted scarf prefers to fall apart. Walls and friendships can do both." Vasco's brain is racing. "A tune however," exclaims Tip Fly . . . "a tune, once composed, can never disintegrate or fall apart and that is where my whole theory breaks down." A foolish grin spreads across Tip Fly's wrinkled face. "Isn't music a wonderful thing."

. . . suddenly the Jungle of Arguments petered out, the bicker bushes parted and there on a vast and sunny plain, picnicking under a lone curly palm, sat the famous Seal of Approval with his immortal thumbs-up sign and a splendid, agreeable smile on his face.

Things just seem to fall apart....
String bags full of oranges
And things within the heart
Calamities evaporate and memories depart.
People laugh at anything.
And things just fall apart.